For all those
Who still believe in the true
Miracle of Christmas

Saint Francis and the Christmas Miracle at Greccio

Written by
Jeffrey Campbell

Illustrated by
Francesca Bianco

Book Layout and Design: Arlene Besore

Edited by: Fr. Alonso de Blas, O.F.M.

Text ©2006—Jeffrey Campbell
Illustrations ©2007—Francesca Bianco

ISBN: 978-0-9796766-3-5

Published and printed by Tau publishing, Phoenix, Arizona
September 2007
First Edition

For re-orders and other inspirational books, CDs and Cards,
visit us online at
Tau-publishing.com

Legend has it the Christmas Crèche or Nativity Scene
as it is commonly called, began in Italy
in 1223, when St. Francis of Assisi,
re-created the Bethlehem scene
at Greccio.

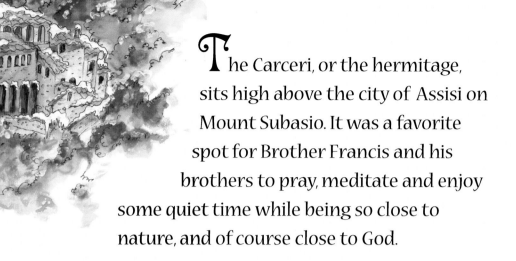

The Carceri, or the hermitage, sits high above the city of Assisi on Mount Subasio. It was a favorite spot for Brother Francis and his brothers to pray, meditate and enjoy some quiet time while being so close to nature, and of course close to God.

This winter night in December was no exception. The stars, however, seemed so very different from before. For some reason they were brighter than on any other night Brother Francis had ever experienced.

"Francis, Francis, why are you lying in the snow peering up into the night sky?"

"Rufino, look; can you see it?"

"See what?" Brother Rufino asked.

"Lie here next to me; I'll show you."

"Francis, the snow is so cold."

"Oh Rufino, perfect joy!"

"I know, I know, everything difficult in our life is perfect joy. Who signed me up for this anyway?" Brother Rufino joked.

Brother Francis laughed as his brother did exactly what he was told to do.

"Look, Rufino, there in the sky, see that star dancing about?"

"I see a million stars up there. Which one are you looking at?"

"That one just above the tall oak tree. Can you see it?" Brother Francis asked again. "See how it is dancing in the sky."

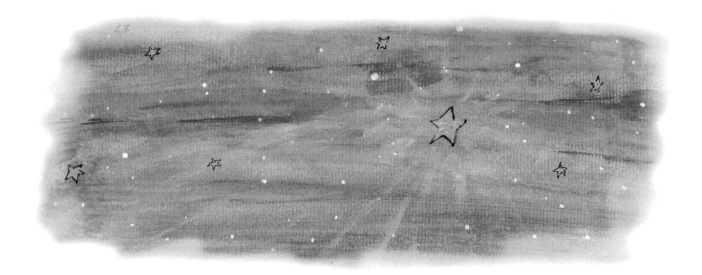

Brother Rufino looked once more at the place Brother Francis had pointed out and this time he could see it.

"It's beautiful, Francis, now can we get up out of the snow?"

"Rufino, why would you not want to take advantage of this wonderful gift God has given us this night?"

While he was saying this, Brother Francis stood up and turned his head toward his brother, giving him that look, the one that meant: listen and be still, there is an important message here. "Look, even our little brother Andiamo is excited."

"Rufino, wake our brothers; we are going to follow that star."

Brother Rufino was a little confused, but knew Brother Francis wasn't joking, so he quickly rose to his feet, brushed the snow from his habit, and ran toward his brothers who were sleeping inside a small cave.

"Wake up! Wake up! We're off to follow a star." They all ignored Brother Rufino; they knew he often liked to play jokes on them, so they were not going to take the bait so late at night. But when Brother Francis came running behind him, shouting the same words, they knew they needed to get up quickly.

"A star is calling out to us this night and we must follow it and see where it leads," Brother Francis told them.

$\mathcal{S}$o the brothers gathered their meager belongings and followed Brother Francis through the forest guided by the brilliant dancing star. "We'll stop at the Portiuncula and get the rest of the brothers, so they can share in this with us," Brother Francis told them as they made their way down Mt. Subasio.

All the friars knew not to question Brother Francis when he was so determined, so they began to share in the same joy that had taken over the heart of their humble leader. Besides, if it was God leading them on this journey they knew the end would bring a wonderful reward.

They arrived at the little church of the Portiuncula just as the sun was beginning to make its way above the horizon. As it began peeking through the forest surrounding their little church, Brother Francis spoke to all of them, "We'll rest now and begin the journey again at dusk."

Brother Leo saw them coming in the distance and shouted out to them.
"Francis and my good brothers, how was your time away? But why are you back so early; weren't you going to spend a couple of more days up there before coming back for the Christmas celebration in Assisi?"

Brother Rufino took a step back, as Brother Francis' hands began speaking even before the words came out of his mouth. He knew from experience that when Brother Francis was so passionate about something, he'd best move out of his way, or risk a bruising from his flying arms.

By now all of them gathered around Brother Francis, as he told them how the star danced in the night sky, and why he felt compelled to see where it would lead them.

"Where do you think it will take us?" Brother Matteo asked.

"I am sure it will be someplace very special," Brother Francis answered.
"After all, it's almost Christmas!"

Christmas was the most important time of the year for Brother Francis and his brothers.

What a gift God has given us in Jesus, he would so often tell them. Year after year he would remind them how wonderful it was for God to share with us his love through His Son Jesus. It's almost too much to comprehend.

It was Brother Francis' desire that the whole world would one day feel the same way about Christmas as he did.

Little did he know that God had the same desire.

Darkness began to surround the tiny church, and one by one the stars were once more coming to life.

"There it is." Brother Francis pointed up to the sky. His brothers craned their necks to see what was getting their founding father so excited.

The Friars headed off merrily into the countryside, as their tunics, one by one, blended into the darkness.

It was a beautiful night. There was just enough light coming from the moon, so that every step they would need to reach their destination could be taken safely.

$\mathcal{L}$ater on the journey Brother Bernardo turned toward Brother Francis and asked, "Does this trail look familiar to you?"

"Yes, it does." Brother Francis replied.

"I think this is the road we take to Greccio," Brother Bernardo added.

"How wonderful," Brother Francis said. "We can stop there and see if our good friend Sir John wants to join us on our journey."

The morning sun was beginning to rise and Brother Francis didn't want to risk getting off course, so they stopped and rested. They would wait until the sun began setting before beginning the journey again.

The moon slowly replaced the glow of the sun, and the brothers were all trying to be the first one to spot the star again in the evening sky. "There it is," said Brother Silvestro. "It seems to be dancing now more than ever."

They walked joyfully through the night, not tiring or worrying about where they were being led. Just as the sun began to scare the stars away, Brother Francis and the rest of the friars found themselves outside the tiny village of Greccio.

As they began to walk through the center of town, the people there spotted the Friars and began to run toward them. It seems they were loved in Greccio almost as much as they were loved in Assisi.

"Brother Francis, Brother Francis," they called out to him, and across the square a booming voice sounded, "Francis, my brother, what brings you to Greccio so close to Christmas?"

𝔅rother Francis responded in a whimsical tone:

"A star, a star dancing in the night."

Brother Francis' response amused Brother Leo as he turned to Brother Bernardo, "You'd better write that line down."

Brother Bernardo began to laugh; "Do you really think someone will sing that song one day?"

"A star?" Sir John asked quizzically. "Yes, Sir John, a star. Tonight when the sun begins to set and the star reappears, we will once more begin our journey. Would you like to join in and see where it is leading us?"

"I would, but for now come with me; you and your brothers must be starving."

"You are a good man, Sir John."

"No, it is you and your brothers who are truly good."

As night surrounded the small village of Greccio, Brother Francis and his followers began to look for the star that had guided them for the past three nights.

"Where is it, Francis?" Brother Leo asked.

"It's there right above us," Brother Francis answered.

"I see it," said Brother Bernardo, "but it is not dancing in the sky like before."

The rest of the brothers and Sir John looked up at the star.

"So, Francis," Sir John laughed, "it seems your star has decided to sit this one out?"

"It can only mean one thing, my good friend: we have reached our destination. This is where we will celebrate the birth of our Lord."

Sir John was so excited that Brother Francis and the rest of the friars would be spending this Christmas with them.

"Tomorrow is Christmas Eve, let's go to the church and pray." Brother Francis led everyone into the small church at Greccio and as he knelt down he asked God to tell him what he wanted them to do here in this humble little village.

As he prayed into the night, Brother Francis would often look up at the crucifix and smile. He would nod his head in agreement as if God was giving him detailed instructions of what he was to do.

As the sun began to light up the tiny chapel, Brother Francis made the sign of the cross, stood up and motioned to his brothers to follow him.

When they were outside the church, Brother Francis turned to them and said, "It's Christmas Eve, tonight we are going to re-create that wonderful night in Bethlehem."

"How are we going to do that?" one of the brothers asked.

"Francis," Brother Masseo added, "How can we possibly recreate the Nativity?"

Brother Francis ignored their questions, knowing exactly how they were going to do it.

"Bernardo, you take seven or eight of your brothers and go into the forest and gather some fallen timbers, enough to build a life-size stable here in the piazza. Rufino, you go to all the outlying fields with a dozen of your brothers and ask the shepherds if they will bring their oxen and sheep and the other animals here for the night. Brother Leo, I give you the most important task of all. You go from home to home and find a couple who have just given birth to a young boy and see if they will be part of this wonderful celebration this evening. Just be sure it is a new-born baby."

So off they went, each one of them, to finish what had been assigned to them. One by one they returned to the square with the timbers and the animals. All the brothers began to build the stable and the manger the baby would be placed in.

The only one who was having a difficult time was Brother Leo. He couldn't find a newborn anywhere. Brother Leo knew that Brother Francis wouldn't be happy with an older child playing the part, so he began to worry about what he was going to do. He knocked on every door in the city but all he could find was a young newly-married couple who were perfect for the part; however they had not yet borne a child.

It was getting late, and Brother Francis was eager to begin the evening celebration. The stable was built, the manger was sitting empty in the middle surrounded by all the animals that gathered to be part of this wonderful celebration.

Brother Francis looked over at Brother Rufino. "Have you seen Leo?"

Brother Rufino shrugged his shoulders, "Not since early this morning."

Brother Leo paced in front of the home of the couple who would play the part of Mary and Joseph. He prayed continuously to God, asking for help. "You know, God, what this order needs is a Friar who can help us find things." The door opened and Brother Leo asked if he could use a couple of blankets. He took one and rolled it up tight and then wrapped it in the other one. He handed it to the young mother. "This is all we can do. It's going to be very cold tonight, so Francis will think you have wrapped your baby up tight to keep him warm."

Brother Leo didn't feel good about what he had done, and he already started asking God to forgive him. The three of them walked toward the square and the newly erected stable.

"Leo," Brother Francis shouted, "I was getting worried."

"Not to worry, Francis, everything is under control. Mary and Joseph, meet Francis."

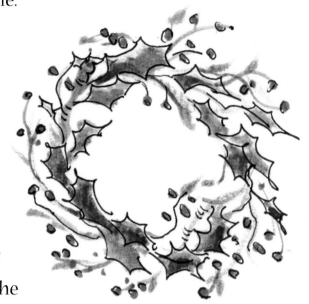

Brother Francis knelt down in front of the couple as if believing it was really the mother of Jesus and her husband.

The young woman gently laid the bundle in the manger and took her place with her husband behind it.

Everyone in the city gathered in the square on this winter's night to witness this historic event. This was a first. No one had ever tried to re-create the Nativity in such a realistic way before. The star that led them to this place was once more dancing delightfully in the sky above the stable, illuminating the newly fallen snow covering the piazza.

ℬrother Francis was kneeling and praying before the manger, and as the crowd of people began to sing, he stood up and turned toward them. Tears were streaming down his face and he could barely control his emotions. When the singing stopped, he began speaking to the crowd.

"My good friends, tonight a savior is born to us. Jesus Christ our King has come to visit his people."

As Brother Leo held the book for him, Brother Francis began to read the Gospel passage about the birth of Jesus, illuminating the words with a small torch.

When Brother Francis finished, he closed the book in Brother Leo's hand, and began to turn toward the manger. Brother Leo was afraid this would happen; he thought Brother Francis might want to hold the child for all to see, so he reached out his arm to stop him so he could tell him what he had done. He knew what he'd done was wrong and how important it was to ask for forgiveness.

"What is it?" Brother Francis asked.

"The baby," Brother Leo whispered.

"Yes, I know," Brother Francis whispered back.

"But you don't understand."

"No, my dear brother, it is you who does not yet understand."

Brother Leo felt terrible. Brother Francis must have discovered his deceitful plan. It was too late; Brother Francis was determined.

The air was calm and silence had covered this Holy Place; there wasn't a sound that could be heard in the entire square, except for the gentle crying of a newborn baby.

"Why couldn't I have found this baby earlier today?" Brother Leo asked himself. "I have let everyone down."

As Brother Leo bowed his head in remorse he felt a calming touch on his shoulder. He turned around but didn't see anyone standing close to him. Yet, a sense of peace suddenly came over him as Brother Francis picked up the bundle from the manger.

Brother Francis held it tightly in his arms, and looking up to heaven gave thanks to God for bringing him to this place and for all those who gathered to celebrate Christmas.

Brother Francis, still holding the tiny bundle in his arms, turned toward the faithful. Once more he said. "Tonight, our savior has come to visit his people."

Brother Francis knelt back down beside the manger. Brother Leo stood up slowly and walked toward Brother Francis. Kneeling down beside him and with tears in his eyes, "Francis, I am so sorry."

"Sorry for what?" Brother Francis asked.

"For not finding a baby to play the part of Jesus."

Francis placed his arms around his dear brother. "Leo, look inside the manger."

Brother Leo wiped the tears away from his eyes and peered into the tiny wooden crib as Brother Francis slowly pulled away the blanket.

"Francis?" Brother Leo could barely get the words out. "How could this be possible?"

"My dear brother; if one only has faith and believes, all things are possible. Jesus is in the hearts of all who have faith, and those who have faith can see Jesus in all things, just as you see him at this moment, in this tiny wooden manger as the infant Jesus."

Brother Leo once more felt a peaceful and calming presence surrounding him and clearly understood it was indeed a miracle that made this all possible. Yes, it was the Christmas Miracle at Greccio, and the beginning of a tradition that lives on to this day as the Christmas Nativity.